Orion Books Ltd
Orion House
5 Upper St Martin's Lane
London WC2H 9EA

First published by Orion in 2001

Drawings by Michael Martin

Cover illustrations by Alex Graham

© Associated Newspapers plc 2001

ISBN 0 75284 435 0

Printed and bound in Great Britain
by Butler & Tanner Ltd, Frome and London

I've just had this dream. I was racing neck and neck with Michael Schumacher around Silverstone...

...and I was just about to overtake him going into Bridge Corner. Totally unrealistic of course—

The approach to Club Corner is a much better place!

AND AGAIN, FRED

DINNER, FRED

Sorry, mate. Knocking-off time!

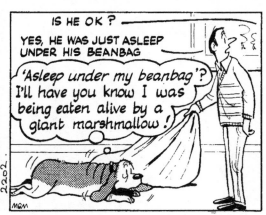

HELLO, FRED. HAVE YOU MISSED ME?

Not really!

With the price of petrol these days, you'd think he'd be pleased we're not using any...

...But, oh no, not him!

WHAT ARE YOU WATCHING, DEAR?

THE HIGHLIGHTS OF COWES WEEK. JUST LOOK AT THOSE FABULOUS YACHTS

COWS? In yachts?

Our assignment today, lads, is to sneak into Satan's garden and swipe that delicious bone of his

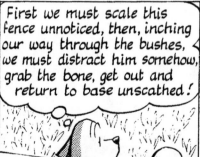

First we must scale this fence unnoticed, then, inching our way through the bushes, we must distract him somehow, grab the bone, get out and return to base unscathed!

I think it just may be a *Mission Impossible!*

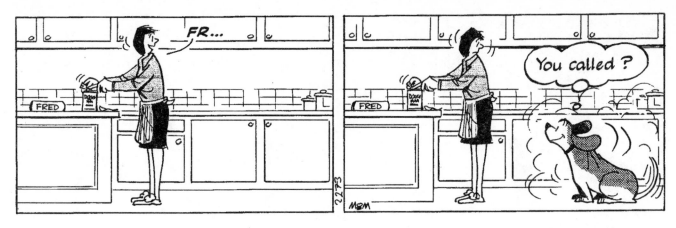

Uh-oh!

It's safe to say that we're not the best of buddies with Harry Hardman and Bruiser!

...AND FINALLY, MADAM, THIS ONE IS OUR BESTSELLER. GOOD VALUE, BUT UNBEATABLE IN ITS RANGE

Oh, good. It's stopped raining!

THANK YOU VERY MUCH. I'LL BRING MY HUSBAND IN SOMETIME

Yes, thank you. It's been a very informative five minutes!

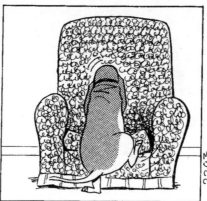

WHAT A LOVELY DOGGY, JAMIE

YES, HE LOOKS LIKE ZANOOK

'ZANOOK'? WHO'S ZANOOK?

Yes, tell us who this Zanook is!

HE'S THAT FUNNY-LOOKING BIG-EARED DWARF IN MY STORY BOOK

You can go off children very quickly, you know!

HAD A NICE WALK?

YES, YOU SHOULD HAVE SEEN FRED CHASING A RABBIT, IT WAS HILARIOUS

DID HE CATCH IT?

WHAT? THE WAY HE LOLLOPS ALONG?

...OF COURSE NOT. POOR OLD FRED WAS LAGGING MILES BEHIND

I'd like to see him do better!

WHAT HAVE YOU DONE TO MY CHOCOLATE SPONGE CAKE?

IT WAS FOR THE CHURCH BAZAAR!

I ONLY HAD A SMALL SLICE, DEAR

She should count herself lucky I didn't get to it first!

Have a heart. She's only nipped into the shops for some Christmas cards...

Well, if that's how you feel...

...she certainly won't be sending one to you!

Here come Spot, Dab, Speck and Blot!

A right dotty lot!

2372.

ARE YOU READY YET?

NEARLY. I'M JUST DOING MY HAIR

WELL, HURRY UP. WE'RE GOING TO BE LATE!

DON'T RUSH ME. I HAVEN'T DECIDED WHAT SHOES TO WEAR YET!

IF YOU DON'T GET A MOVE ON I SHALL GO WITHOUT YOU!

2373.

ALL RIGHT, ALL RIGHT!

I know what you were thinking!